Foreword

All builders need a Ty, to build a warm house and somewhere to sleep safe at night, or even a skyscraper, like the Shard.

From an early age, people like Eliza, Joanna and Deepa inspired me to learn and want to be part of a team - building airports for people to go on holiday, railway stations and roads to help us meet friends and family.

I helped build the Olympic Park in London - people like Chan, Alec, Saad and Chuck were part of our team who made it happen. Building parks and sports venues so that people can have fun and somewhere to cheer a friend or just be a supporter is exciting and uplifting. That's what builders do!

I hope this book encourages mums and dads to help see that being a builder is varied and fun, where we can live our dreams and fulfil ambitions - whilst creating better places to live and enjoy.

Mark Reynolds
Mace, Group Chief Executive
& Construction Leadership Council, Steering Co-ordination Group

Ty

Hi there I'm Ty, and I am the guy,
leading the site team that makes it all fly.

My team is strong, we'd win the Olympics,
The builders can't build without the logistics!

The way it is run is a slick operation,
We make it all flow with some coordination.

We plan all the routes and make the layout,
We manage the traffic that comes in and out.

My team

My team and I, we have an eye,
for dangers and clutter, we never walk by.

We take in materials, we take out the waste,
each item is tracked so it's never misplaced.

We keep the site safe from intruders and fire,
it's kept nice and clean, for all to admire.

We run it like clockwork, and that is a skill,
we take all the headache, the client can chill.

The client

The client is calling, some doors need installing,
we jump right on to it, without any stalling.

Make no mistake, a lot is at stake,
the buyers are touring before the handshake.

I don't want to say it, but if we delay it,
it will cause trouble, so we go survey it.

Let's meet my crew and see what they do,
they all play a part to see this job through.

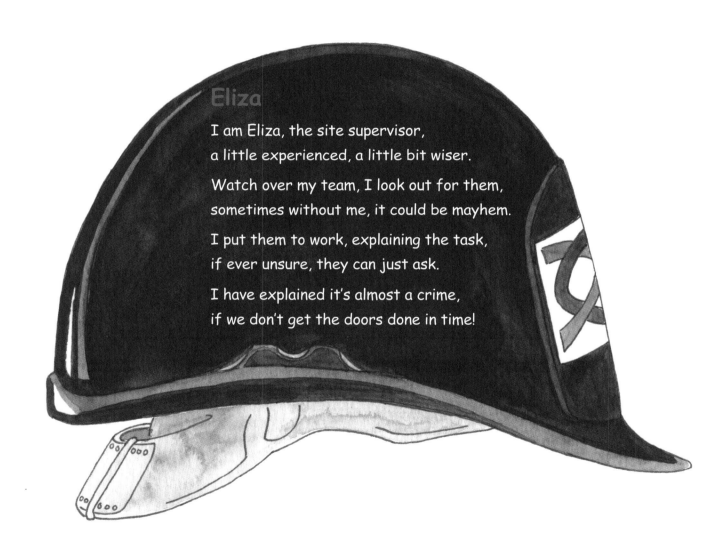

Eliza

I am Eliza, the site supervisor,
a little experienced, a little bit wiser.

Watch over my team, I look out for them,
sometimes without me, it could be mayhem.

I put them to work, explaining the task,
if ever unsure, they can just ask.

I have explained it's almost a crime,
if we don't get the doors done in time!

Joanna

I am Joanna, logistics planner,
I plan the site in an efficient manner.

I draw the plans to show the flow,
of how the vehicles come and go.

I show the movement of people and stuff,
I work out if room on site is enough.

Enough for the wagons to turn or reverse,
enough for the people to flock or disperse.

Deepa

My name is Deepa, I am the storekeeper,
storing off site can also be cheaper.

Sometimes on site there is no space,
the clutter and crowd can get in your face.

All doors are delivered to me in the store,
the site will request it when they need each door.

I pack on to pallets, send only what's needed,
so space on the site is never exceeded.

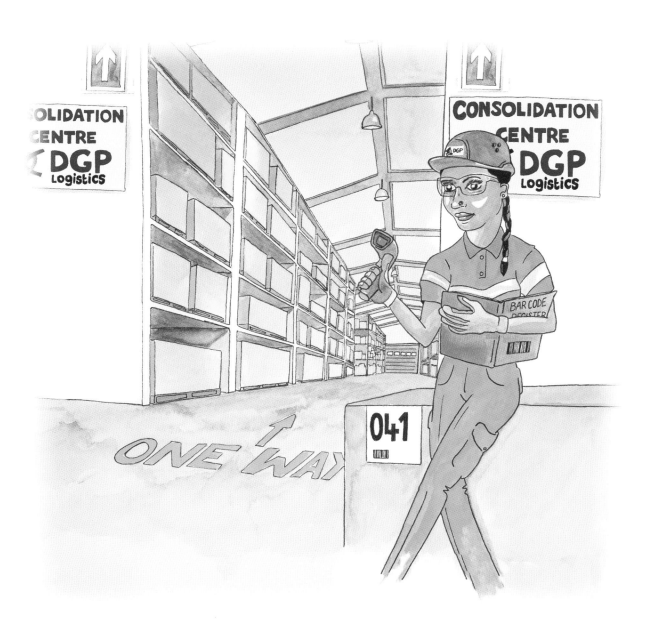

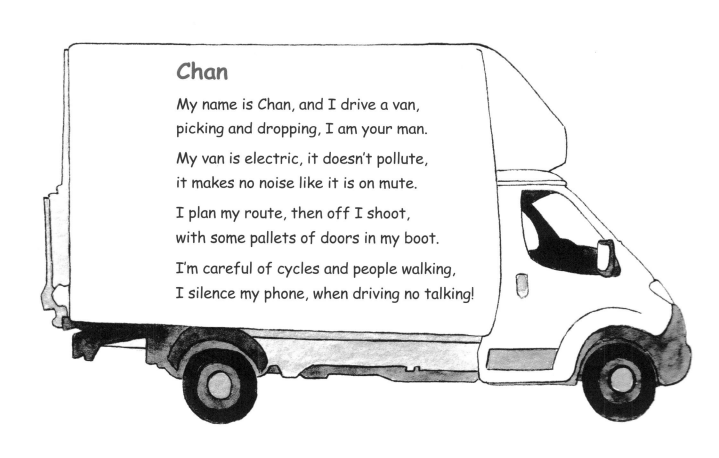

Chan

My name is Chan, and I drive a van,
picking and dropping, I am your man.

My van is electric, it doesn't pollute,
it makes no noise like it is on mute.

I plan my route, then off I shoot,
with some pallets of doors in my boot.

I'm careful of cycles and people walking,
I silence my phone, when driving no talking!

Alec

Hi there I'm Alec, I manage the traffic,
on such a big site it can really get manic.

My clothing is bright, so I keep in sight,
of all of the vehicles that turn up to site.

When lorries arrive, park up and unload,
I watch out for people if crossing the road.

Stop, look and listen, think and then cross,
the doors are delivered, we radio the boss.

Saad

My name is Saad, security guard,
for thieves and intruders, I make it hard.

Sites are not safe for children or pets,
there can be dangers, hazards and threats.

But on some days, with special permission,
you can come visit under supervision.

As you arrive, I meet and greet,
I see you out when your visit's complete.

CHILDREN KEEP OUT!
Construction sites are dangerous

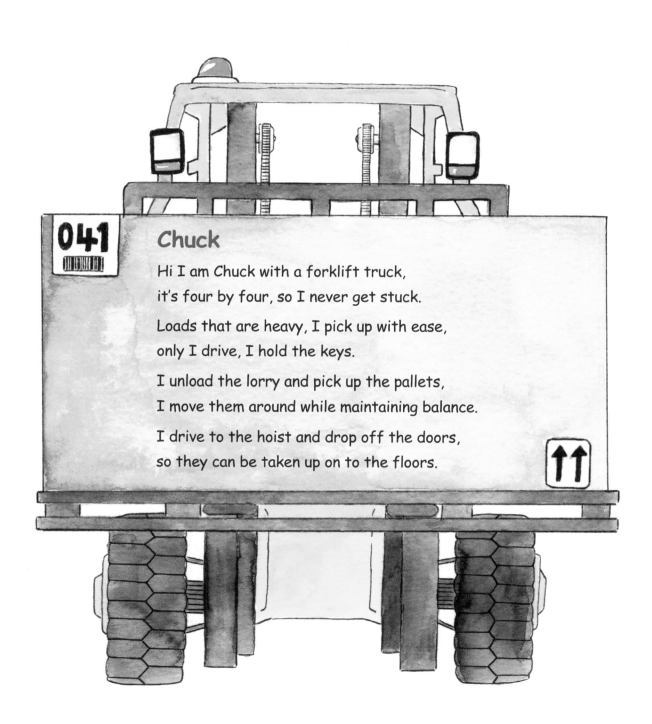

041

Chuck

Hi I am Chuck with a forklift truck,
it's four by four, so I never get stuck.

Loads that are heavy, I pick up with ease,
only I drive, I hold the keys.

I unload the lorry and pick up the pallets,
I move them around while maintaining balance.

I drive to the hoist and drop off the doors,
so they can be taken up on to the floors.

Elzbieta

I'm Elzbieta, the hoist operator,
a hoist is a lift, some say elevator.

I go to the top to some dizzying heights,
where I get to see all the beautiful sights.

Just press the button and I'll be there,
up or down taking people and gear.

I take up the doors where they are required,
the chippie is happy with what he's acquired.

Surinder

Hi I'm Surinder, I am the carpenter,
I'm wearing some gloves so I don't get a splinter.

I'm sawing and chopping the doors down to size,
I'm wearing some glasses to shield my eyes.

If I drop my hammer, have any mishaps,
I'm wearing my boots with steel toe-caps.

Locks and handles, I check the tilt,
I hang the doors on the frames I built.

Dean

Hi there I'm Dean, I keep it all clean,
the office, the showers, the kitchen, canteen.

When I keep it tidy, my colleagues are happy,
they work with a smile and don't get so snappy.

I kill all the germs from the handles they clutch,
and surfaces on all the doors they touch.

Washing my hands, I cleanse and I freshen,
a sparkling site makes a good impression.

Fire point

Jordan

Hi there I'm Jordan, the head fire warden,
to keep people out, I put up a cordon.

Extinguisher, that puts out fires,
I check it and change it, if it expires.

If there's a fire, I raise the alarm,
evacuate all, away from harm.

One hour rated, itself it closes,
the door buys time for the folks with the hoses.

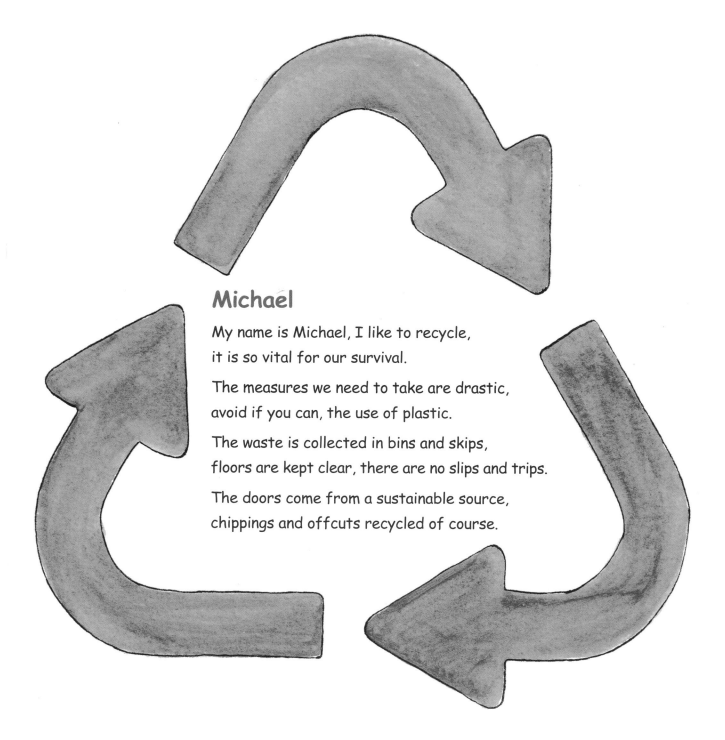

Michael

My name is Michael, I like to recycle,
it is so vital for our survival.

The measures we need to take are drastic,
avoid if you can, the use of plastic.

The waste is collected in bins and skips,
floors are kept clear, there are no slips and trips.

The doors come from a sustainable source,
chippings and offcuts recycled of course.

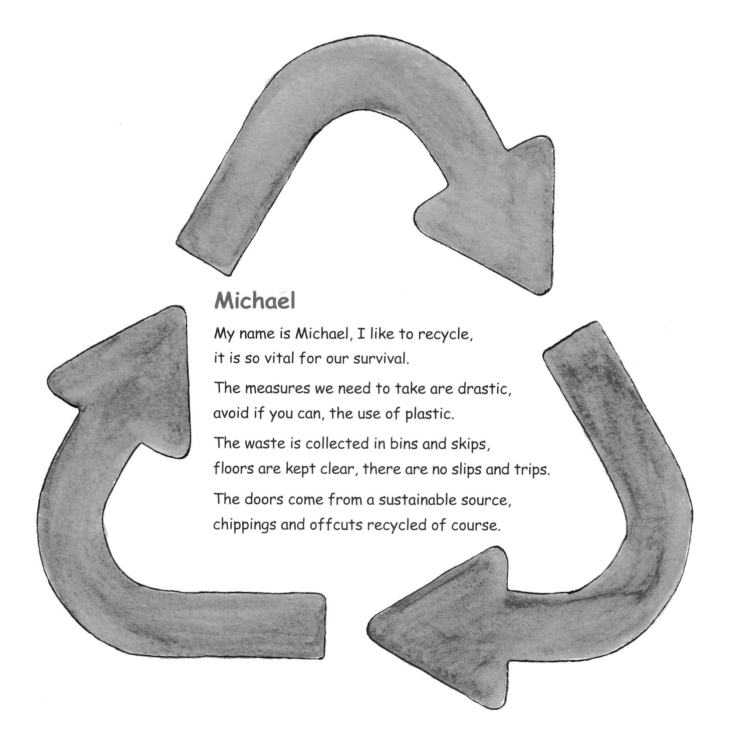

Michael

My name is Michael, I like to recycle,
it is so vital for our survival.

The measures we need to take are drastic,
avoid if you can, the use of plastic.

The waste is collected in bins and skips,
floors are kept clear, there are no slips and trips.

The doors come from a sustainable source,
chippings and offcuts recycled of course.

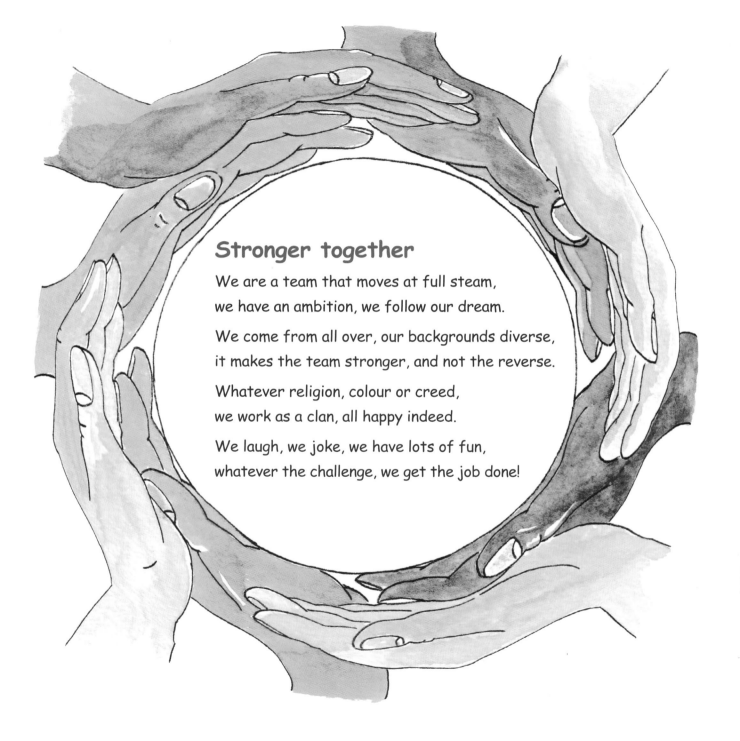

Stronger together

We are a team that moves at full steam,
we have an ambition, we follow our dream.

We come from all over, our backgrounds diverse,
it makes the team stronger, and not the reverse.

Whatever religion, colour or creed,
we work as a clan, all happy indeed.

We laugh, we joke, we have lots of fun,
whatever the challenge, we get the job done!

All profits from the sales of this book go to projects supporting
local communities and construction related charities.